FORESTRY COMMISSION BULLETIN 99

1·75

Urban Trees –

A survey of street trees in England

S.J. Hodge

Arboriculturist, Forestry Commission

Department of the Environment Arboriculture Contract

LONDON: HMSO

ISBN 0 11 710299 7
FDC 273 : 524.6 : (410)

KEYWORD: Arboriculture

Enquiries relating to this publication
should be addressed to:
The Technical Publications Officer,
Forestry Commission, Forest Research Station,
Alice Holt Lodge, Wrecclesham,
Farnham, Surrey, GU10 4LH.

Acknowledgements
The work reported in this Bulletin was funded
by the Department of the Environment.

S. M. Colderick (formerly of Silviculture (South)
Branch) supervised much of the data collection
and R. C. Boswell (Statistics and Computing
Branch (South)) undertook the task of data
analysis.

Front cover: A healthy silver maple improving the
visual amenity of a Milton Keynes housing estate.
(39505)
Inset. A recently planted red oak standard struggling
for survival. Strood, Kent.

Contents

Urban Trees –
A survey of street trees in England

Summary

In 1989 a survey of 3600 urban street trees was carried out in 30 towns and cities throughout England by the Forestry Commission with funding from the Department of the Environment.

Five genera, *Acer, Sorbus, Prunus, Betula* and *Tilia,* constituted 70% of trees surveyed. The mean shoot extension over all species was 12.4 cm, a growth rate considered to be, on average, about 60% of the potential in urban situations. For the survey as a whole, 80% of the trees were judged to be in good condition; visually improving the urban landscape.

Of trees surveyed, 15% had significant damage and 1.5% of the trees surveyed had been snapped off by vandals. Of trees planted in shrub beds only 0.7% had been vandalised compared with 1.9% of trees planted in paved areas and grass. Damage to tree stems was much more frequent in paved and grass areas than in shrub or herbaceous beds. Dead trees constituted 2.1% of street trees encountered.

The average age of trees surveyed was 25 years. Of trees over 50 years old only 26% were found in town centres, the remaining 74% being in suburban areas.

Most of the frequently encountered species showed steadily declining shoot extension, even while still young. Despite this trend, older trees surveyed tended to be in better condition than younger, especially recently planted, trees.

The most common planting position encountered was grass, in which 43.5% of trees surveyed were growing. Of trees over 50 years old 75% were growing in grass and only 7% in shrub beds. Of trees 15 years old or less, 27% were planted in grass and 30% in shrub beds.

Trees planted in shrub and herbaceous beds showed greater mean shoot extension (13.7 cm and 15.3 cm respectively) than trees planted in paved areas (12.7 cm) or grass (11.4 cm).

Les Arbres en Ville – Etude des arbres plantés dans les rues d'Angleterre

Résumé

En 1989, 3600 arbres plantés dans les rues de 30 villes anglaises, furent l'objet d'une étude menée par la Forestry Commission et financée par le Département de l'Environnement.

70% des arbres étudiés appartenaient à cinq genres différents: *Acer, Sorbus, Prunus, Betula* et *Tilia*. L'accroissement annuel moyen des pousses, observé pour l'ensemble des essences, était de 12,4 cm, ce qui représente un taux de croissance équivalant, en moyenne, à 60% du potentiel de développement dans un contexte urbain. Les résultats de l'étude révélèrent que 80% des arbres, tous genres confondus, étaient en bonne condition et qu'ils contribuaient à l'embellissement du paysage urbain.

Parmi les arbres examinés, 15% avaient été endommagés sérieusement et 1,5% avaient été cassés par des vandales. Seulement 0,7% des arbres plantés dans des parterres d'arbustes furent vandalisés contre 1,9% des arbres plantés dans l'herbe ou dans des zones pavées. Les dégâts causés aux troncs d'arbres étaient beaucoup plus fréquents dans les zones pavées ou les zones d'herbes que dans les parterres d'arbustes ou de plantes herbacées. 2,1% des arbres étudiés dans les rues étaient des arbres morts.

La moyenne d'âge des arbres étudiés était de 25 ans. Seulement 26% des arbres de plus de 50 ans se trouvaient dans les centres-villes tandis que 74% d'entre eux se trouvaient dans les zones de banlieue.

La majorité des essences les plus répandues révélèrent une diminution de l'accroissement annuel des pousses, même pour les plus jeunes d'entre elles. Malgré cette tendance, l'étude indiqué que les arbres les plus vieux semblaient être en meilleure condition que les arbres les plus jeunes, particulièrement si ceux-ci avaient été plantés récemment.

L'environnement le plus souvent rencontré pour la plantation des arbres fut l'herbe; ainsi, 43,5% des arbres étudiés poussaient dans l'herbe. 75% des arbres de plus de 50 ans poussaient dans l'herbe contre 7% dans des parterres d'arbustes. 27% des arbres de 15 ans maximum poussaient dans l'herbe tandis que 30% d'entre eux poussaient dans des parterres d'arbustes.

Pour les arbres plantés dans les parterres d'arbustes et de plantes herbacées, l'accroissement annuel moyen des pousses était plus important (respectivement 13,7 cm et 15,3 cm) que celui des arbres plantés dans des zones pavées (12,7 cm) ou dans l'herbe (11,4 cm).

Bäume in der Stadt – Eine begutachtung von Straßenbäumen in England

Zusammenfassung

1989 wurde von der Forstverwaltung eine Untersuchung von 3600 Straßenbäumen in 30 Städten in ganz England durchgeführt, deren Finanzierung durch das Umweltministerium erfolgte.

Fünf Gattungen, *Acer, Sorbus, Prunus, Betula* und *Tilia,* machten 70% der begutachteten Bäume aus. Der mittlere jährliche Triebzuwachs aller Baumarten war 12,4 cm, eine Wachstumsrate, die im Durchschnitt als ca. 60% des Potentials in Stadtgebieten angesehen wird. Im großen und ganzen wurde in der Untersuchung festgestellt, daß 80% der Bäume in gutem Zustand waren und die städtische Landschaft optisch verschönerten.

Bei 15% der begutachteten Bäume wurden wesentliche Schäden festgestellt, und 1,5% der begutachteten Bäume waren mutwillig abgebrochen worden. Von den in Strauchrabatten angepflanzten Bäumen wurden nur 0,7% mutwillig beschädigt, im Vergleich zu 1,9% der Bäume, die in gepflasterten Bereichen und im Gras angepflanzt waren. Schäden am Baumstamm wurden öfter in gepflasterten Bereichen und im Gras festgestellt, als in Strauch- oder Staudenrabatten. Die abgestorbenen Bäume machten 2,1% der begutachteten Straßenbäume aus.

Das durchschnittliche Alter der begutachteten Bäume war 25 Jahre und von den über 50 Jahre alten Bäumen standen nur 26% in Stadtzentren; die übrigen 74% befanden sich in Vorstadtgebieten.

Die meisten der oft angetroffenen Baumarten wiesen einen ständig zurückgehenden Triebzuwachs auf, was sogar bei den jungen Bäumen der Fall war. Trotz dieses Trends waren die älteren begutachteten Bäume gewöhnlich in besserem Zustand als die jüngeren, und besonders als diejenigen, die erst vor kurzem angepflanzt wurden.

Die am meisten angetroffene Anpflanzstelle war im Gras, in dem 43,5% der begutachteten Bäume wuchsen. Von den über 50 jährigen Bäumen wuchsen 75% im Gras und nur 7% in Strauchrabatten. Von den 15 jährigen oder jüngeren Bäumen standen 27% im Gras und 30% in Strauchrabatten.

In Strauch- und Staudenrabatten angepflanzte Bäume wiesen einen größeren mittleren jährlichen Triebzuwachs auf (13,7 cm bzw. 15,3 cm) als die in gepflasterten Bereichen (12,7 cm) oder im Gras (11,4 cm) stehenden.

Urban Trees – A survey of street trees in England

S.J. Hodge, *Arboriculturist, Forestry Commission*

Introduction

Little information is available on the growth rates of urban trees. Trees that survive the establishment phase often put on so little growth that they appear moribund. Conversely, problems occur when a fast growing or large species is successfully established and 'outgrows' its living space.

There is a need to build up a database of information on the structure and health of the urban tree population in order to determine recommendations that will improve the planning and design of urban tree planting and the performance of trees once planted. Funding from the Department of the Environment enabled a survey to be undertaken in 1989 by Forestry Commission Research Division staff. This survey encompassed 3600 trees, made up of 120 trees in each of 30 randomly selected towns and cities throughout England.

Survey method

The towns and cities were selected on a random basis, with a weighting given to population. An alphabetical list was made of all towns and cities in England with a population of over 30 000. The cumulative total population of these towns and cities was determined (29 141 562) and divided by 30 (971 502). Locations were selected that corresponded to every 971 502 interval of the cumulative population within the alphabetical list. The places thus selected were:

Altrincham	Leeds
Birkenhead	Liverpool
Birmingham	Manchester
Bradford	Morley
Bristol	Norwich
Camden	Peterlee
Chesterfield	Reading
Croydon	Runcorn
Durham	Sheffield
Exeter	Southwark
Greenwich	Strood
Haringey	Tower Hamlets
Hemel Hempstead	Wandsworth
Huddersfield	Widnes
Kingston upon Hull	York

Of the 120 trees assessed at each location, 60 trees were in the town or city centre and 60 were in a suburb. The starting point of the survey in each case was selected at random. Using a street map of the place, x and y axes were marked around the town centre and a suburban area (also selected at random). Random numbers (easting first, then northing) located the point to start the survey. Prior to visiting and without any detailed knowledge of the location, a survey route was drawn on the map; this was followed until 60 trees had been assessed.

All trees on the survey route were assessed provided:

branch tips of the tree were reachable (using 2 m high step-ladders);
the trees were not more than 5 metres from the edge of the carriageway or pavement;
it was considered that the trees were planted as urban trees and were not present before development;
trees had not been pollarded in the last 5 years.

The information recorded was as follows.
1. Shoot extension (10 shoots per tree were

measured from the ends of main branches around the outside of the crown; five lateral shoots and five apical shoots).

2. Age (subjectively estimated to within the nearest 10 years, using experience gained from previous urban tree research).
3. Planting position (grass, paved, shrub and herbaceous). Entries for trees planted in a position borderline between these categories were indicated as such.
4. General condition score (on a subjectively assessed 1 to 3 scale, from not fulfilling any useful role in visually improving the urban landscape to totally fulfilling that role, within the constraint of the tree's current size).
5. Damage (damage likely to be affecting the growth, potential and appearance of the tree; assessed as present or not and on what part of the tree).
6. Soil type (of a sample augered from 15 cm depth. The sample was taken near to the base of the tree, to avoid problems of sampling away from the tree in areas with tarmac or paving; assessed as either sand, sandy loam, loam, clay loam, clay).

7. Species group.

Species and varieties were grouped for two main reasons.

1. In order to accumulate adequate data for the common groups, species and varieties that did not appear to show marked differences in growth rates were grouped together. When a particular species in a group showed a marked difference in growth rate, it was kept separate.
2. Some grouping of varieties was required due to identification difficulties, particularly as the survey was started during the winter months.

Results

General findings

Species distribution

The frequency of occurrence of all genera surveyed is shown in Figure 1. Five genera constituted 70% of trees surveyed, with *Acer* alone accounting for 21.5% and *Sorbus* 18.4%. In all, 39 genera were recorded but 22 of these together made up only 4.5% of the survey total and hence are grouped together in the 'other' category in Figure 1.

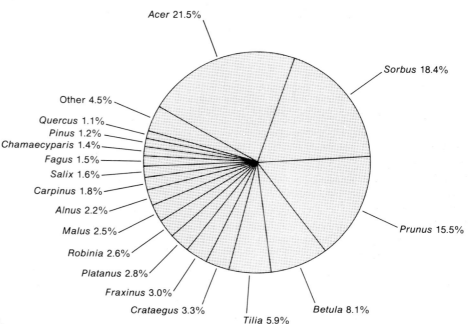

Figure 1. Distribution of trees surveyed by genus.

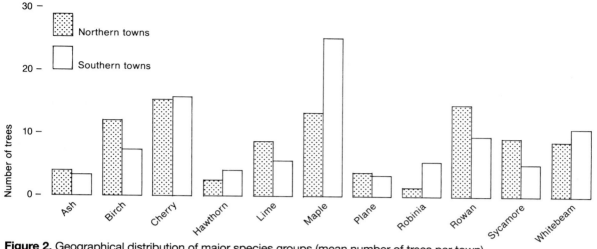

Figure 2. Geographical distribution of major species groups (mean number of trees per town).

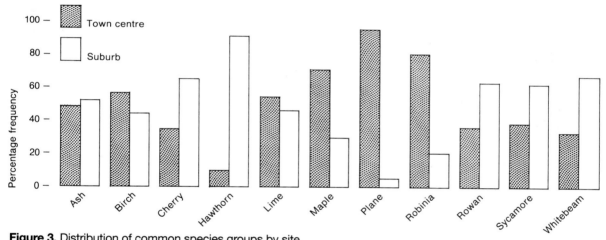

Figure 3. Distribution of common species groups by site.

Details of all species groups surveyed are given in Appendix 1. For the purposes of statistical analysis, the 11 major species groups were used, making up 78.3% of the urban trees surveyed. These species groups are, in decreasing order of occurrence: maple, cherry, rowan, birch, whitebeam, lime, sycamore, ash, plane, hawthorn and false acacia (*Robinia*).

A low population of maple and false acacia was recorded in the northern towns (Chesterfield and northwards) included in the survey, as well as high populations of birch, lime, rowan and sycamore (Figure 2).

Maple, plane and false acacia were more commonly recorded in town centres, whilst cherry, hawthorn, rowan, sycamore and whitebeam were more frequent in suburban areas (Figure 3). The reasons for this distribution might be the type of planting scheme undertaken and the perceptions of the designer as to which species are appropriate for, and will survive in, suburban or urban areas.

Tree growth

The mean shoot extension over all species was 12.4 cm, and only 185 trees (5% of survey) had a mean shoot extension of 30 cm or more (Figure 4). Appendix 1 details mean growth rates by

3

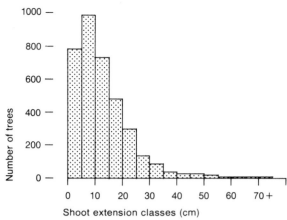

Figure 4. Distribution of shoot extension classes; all species.

did not detect any significant correlations. Even so, the effect of climatic variation on growth has been removed from subsequent analyses. In addition, there were no large statistically significant differences in the shoot extension of the most commonly occurring species groups between town centre and suburban areas.

Tree condition

For the survey as a whole, 80% of the trees were judged to be in good condition, fulfilling their role in the landscape in terms of visual amenity. This is remarkably high, particularly in view of the considerable and numerous problems facing arboriculturists and foresters in the urban environment. Of the 20% of trees judged not to be in good condition (condition scores 2 and 3), 5% were recorded as not fulfilling any beneficial role in the landscape (condition score 3).

The condition of some species groups varied greatly from the mean (Figure 5). Of the more frequently recorded species groups, well below the mean were pine (50%) and rowan (65%). Substantially above the mean were plum (92%), beech (89%), willow (89%), apple (88%), horse chestnut (87%) and lime (86%). It is important not to consider the performance of amenity trees on growth parameters alone; of the species in generally good condition only willow showed particularly good growth rates.

Rowan, which accounts for 10.4% of the trees surveyed, had a low percentage in good condition whilst whitebeam, its close relative, had above

species. This information must be combined with knowledge of likely ultimate tree size and form (Hodge and White, 1990) in order to ensure that appropriate species are chosen for urban planting schemes, and to reduce the incidence of trees that have outgrown their living space (Plate 1), trees totally out of scale with their surroundings (Plate 2) and costly commitments to regular pollarding and pruning.

Despite the wide geographical range of locations surveyed, no relationships were apparent between location and shoot extension. Multiple regression analysis, comparing mean summer temperature and rainfall at any location (derived from Met. Office data) with the shoot extension of the most commonly occurring species,

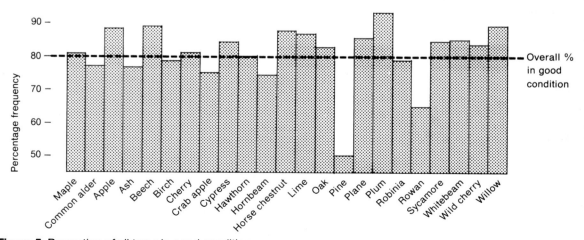

Figure 5. Proportion of all trees in good condition.

4

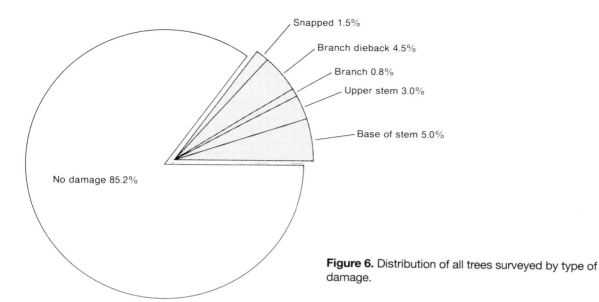

Figure 6. Distribution of all trees surveyed by type of damage.

average. With the exception of cypress, evergreen conifers surveyed were in a generally poor condition. Continuous and relatively intensive particulate deposition on needles, which may be retained for several years, contributes to the often poor growth and sparse and dirty appearance of conifers in urban areas. Conifer species accounted for only 3.4% of the trees surveyed.

There was no apparent variation in tree condition due to geographical location of town or between town centre and suburban areas.

Damage to trees

Of trees surveyed 85% had no significant damage (Figure 6). Of the damage that was recorded, damage by mowers, strimmers, vehicles, metal grilles and paving slabs to the base of the stem (Plates 3 and 4) and branch dieback (mainly on recently transplanted trees) (Plate 5) were the most common. Only 1.5% of the trees surveyed had been snapped off by vandals, despite the fact that 29.5% of trees surveyed were between 0 and 15 years old (i.e. prone to vandalism).

Stem damage was more frequent in suburban areas than town centres (Figure 7) probably due to the higher risk of damage from vehicles and grass cutting equipment. Snapped trees were also recorded more frequently in suburban areas than in town centres. This could be due to

the congregating habits of those intent on damaging trees and casual opportunities for vandalism, but must also be linked to the high proportion of trees planted in shrub beds in town centres, shrubs acting as a deterrent to vandals (Plate 6). The high incidence of branch dieback in town centres is a reflection of the relatively high numbers of recently planted trees.

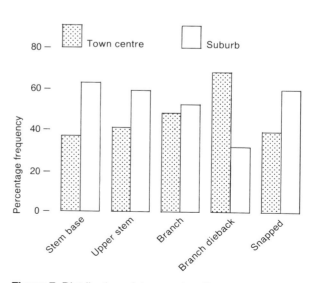

Figure 7. Distribution of damage by site.

5

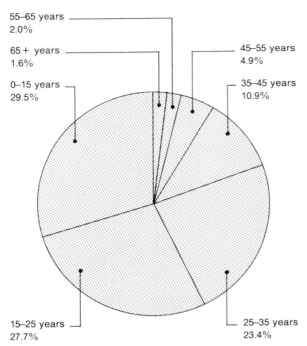

55–65 years
2.0%

65 + years
1.6%

0–15 years
29.5%

45–55 years
4.9%

35–45 years
10.9%

15–25 years
27.7%

25–35 years
23.4%

Figure 8. Age class distribution of all species surveyed.

Table 1. Variation in shoot extension of the major species groups explained by tree age using multiple regression analysis.

Species	% variation in shoot extension accounted for by age	Significance level
Maple	—	$P<0.001$
Ash	6.2%	$P<0.001$
Birch	11.6%	$P<0.001$
Cherry	—	$P<0.001$
Hawthorn	30.0%	$P<0.001$
Lime	1.9%	$P<0.001$
Plane	—	$P<0.001$
False acacia	14.2%	$P<0.001$
Rowan	3.9%	$P<0.001$
Sycamore	24.6%	$P<0.001$
Whitebeam	13.0%	$P<0.001$

Tree age

Distribution

Of trees surveyed 81% were judged to be under 35 years old (Figure 8) and the average age of trees surveyed was 25. The survey method tended to exclude some of the older trees encountered by only recording trees with reachable branch tips and trees judged to be planted as urban trees (and not retained from before development took place) and by not recording recently pollarded trees. However, the number of trees thus excluded was, in practice, small. Factors likely to contribute to this low average age are: repeated failure to establish urban trees successfully, replacement of trees at each cycle of development and increasing awareness of trees as an asset in the urban environment leading to increasing levels of planting.

In some cases individual species groups showed age structures very different from that of the survey population as a whole (Figure 9), indicating changing trends in species choice. Of the more frequently recorded species groups,

maple, alder, birch, cypress, hornbeam, false acacia and rowan are being used increasingly in preference to ash, beech, crab apple, hawthorn, horse chestnut, lime, oak, sycamore and willow. This change of emphasis in species choice will obviously have the eventual effect of changing the species structure of the urban tree population.

Of trees over 50 years old, 74% were found in suburban areas, while trees in younger age groups were fairly evenly distributed, possibly indicating a recent increase in new or replacement planting in town centres and a declining trend of tree planting in suburban areas.

Variation in growth with tree age

As would be expected, the survey found that the shoot extension of most species groups declined with increasing tree age. It is notable, however, that all of the seven major species in Figure 10, apart from cherry, showed steadily declining shoot extension from soon after planting. (Other species are excluded from Figure 10 due to the lack of data for trees in every age class.)

Regression analysis was used to indicate the importance of tree age as a determinant of shoot extension (Table 1). Over 20% of the variation in 1988 shoot extension of hawthorn and sycamore was explained by tree age, probably as many old slow growing specimens of these species were recorded. The other species groups, having a younger average age, have shown less (though

Plate 1. *Scots pine that has out-grown its living space. Fleet, Hampshire.* (38301)

Plate 2. *Sycamore retained during development and totally out of scale with adjacent buildings. Blaydon, Tyne and Wear.* (38365)

Plate 3. *Severe stem damage on a lime tree in Croydon. Damage to the upper stem is caused by the regularly parked lorry; and that at the base of the stem results from a restricted rooting zone causing serious deformation.*

Plate 4. *Damage to the base of a plane tree in Liverpool due to restrictive stake and paving.*

Plate 6. *Dense shrub beds are an effective deterrent to vandals; and to urban tree assessors! Peterlee, Co. Durham.*

Plate 5. *Ugly branch dieback on half-standard Japanese maple in Sheffield in the year after planting.*

Plate 7. *Lime near Caen, Normandy, in August of the second year after planting. Competition resulting from lack of weed control has been made worse by fertilising, leaving the trees in extremely poor condition. This, and the extremely high stakes, will lessen the chances of survival to maturity.*

Plate 8. *Cherry in Liverpool showing severe tie strangulation.*

Plate 9. *Total failure of a high prestige, high cost planting scheme in Glasgow using half-standard stock (photograph taken in August).* (38429)

Plate 10. *Effective planting of wild cherry and field maple in shrub beds on a new housing estate in Widnes (photograph taken in spring).*

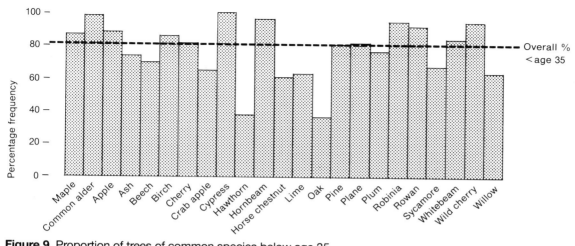

Figure 9. Proportion of trees of common species below age 35.

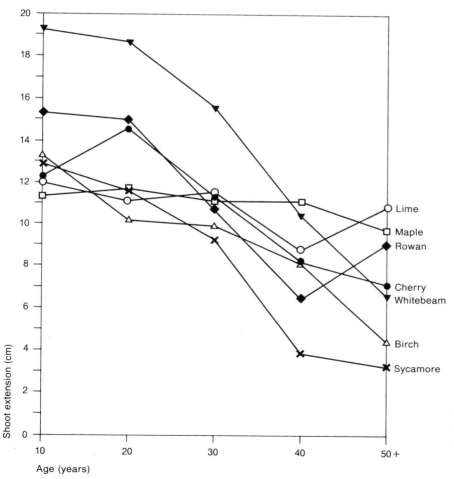

Figure 10. The influence of age on shoot extension.

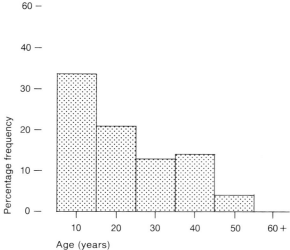

Figure 11. Proportion of trees not in good condition by age class.

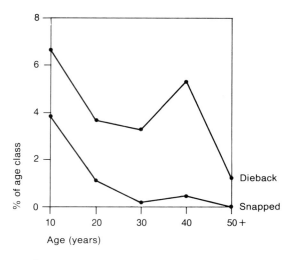

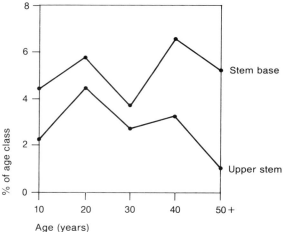

Figure 12. The relationship between tree age and damage

still statistically significant) reduction in growth with age. The effect of tree age on growth has been removed from subsequent analyses.

Variation in condition with tree age

Older trees surveyed tended to be in better condition than younger trees (Figure 11). Care was taken not to allow the size of the tree *per se* to bias condition scoring; a recently planted healthy tree with a good form would receive a good condition score. Of trees under 15 years old, 34% were judged to be in less than good condition. The severe shock of outplanting large stock into inhospitable and ill prepared sites, damage by tree guards, ties and stakes, and vandalism are major contributory factors. The continuing trend of improving tree condition with increasing tree age into the older age classes is influenced by the removal of poor trees before they reach maturity.

Variation in damage with tree age

The incidence of snapped trees and trees with dieback tended to decrease with increasing tree age (Figure 12); most of this type of damage being associated with recently planted trees. The frequency of both damage to the base of the stem and upper stem showed two peaks, at 20 years and 40 years. The reasons for this inter-

esting distribution of stem damage by tree age is not clear. The first peak may be due to damage caused by stakes, ties and grilles (Plate 7); and the second to the additional cumulative effect of damage from vehicles and grass cutting equipment, troughs indicating periods after removal of trees in poor condition.

Planting position

Distribution

Despite the survey excluding trees in parks, the most common planting position encountered was grass (Figure 13) in which 43.5% of the

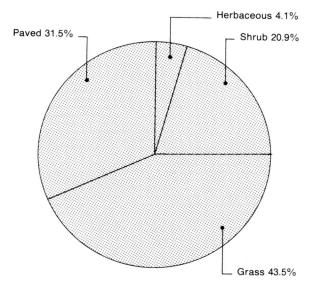

Paved 31.5%

Herbaceous 4.1%

Shrub 20.9%

Grass 43.5%

Figure 13. Distribution of trees surveyed by planting position.

trees were growing. Trees in paved areas constituted 31.5% of those surveyed and trees in shrubs and herbaceous beds 25%.

Trends in choice of planting position have changed over time (Figure 14). Of trees over 50 years old, 75% were growing in grass, compared with only 27% of trees 15 years old or less. Of trees over 50 years old, 7% were in shrub beds in contrast to 30% of trees 15 years old or less. The proportion of trees in paved areas appears to be relatively constant up to trees of 40 years of age. The lower numbers of older trees found in pavements may be due to such trees being removed as root-induced pavement and kerb damage develops.

The survey recorded extreme variation between towns in the choice of planting positions.

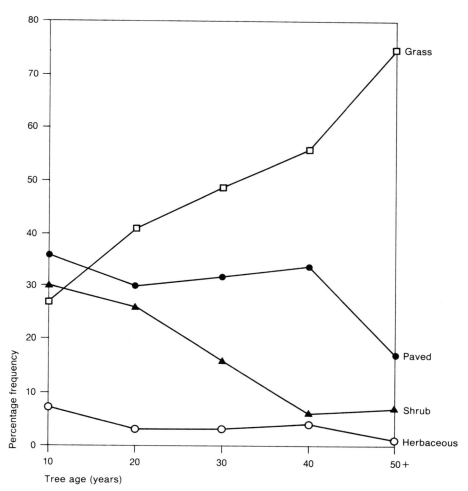

Grass

Paved

Shrub

Herbaceous

Percentage frequency

Tree age (years)

Figure 14. Proportion of trees in each planting position by age class.

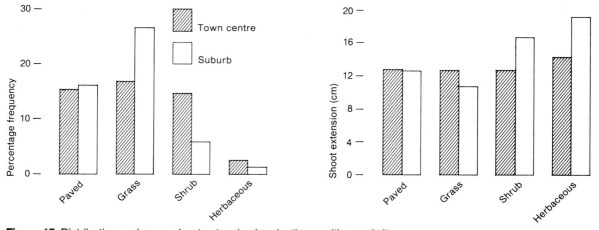

Figure 15. Distribution and mean shoot extension by planting position and site.

Although only 120 trees recorded per location is too small a sample to draw firm conclusions, these variations may indicate differences in policies and opportunities for urban tree planting between local authorities.

Trees planted in grass were more frequently recorded in suburban areas than in town centres (Figure 15), due mainly to the high incidence of trees in grass strips between pavement and road on many residential estates. Conversely, trees in shrub and herbaceous beds were more frequently recorded in town centres, particularly associated with the widespread trend towards town centre redevelopment and pedestrian precincts.

Variation in tree growth with planting position

Trees planted in shrub and herbaceous beds showed greater mean shoot extension (13.7 cm and 15.3 cm respectively) than trees planted in paved areas (12.7 cm) or grass (11.4 cm) (Figure 16). Competition for moisture, and to a lesser extent, nutrients is most intense with aggressive grass sward, less in shrub beds and less still in herbaceous beds. In addition, shrub and herbaceous beds have a relatively large area of well prepared soil for tree root growth. Trees in paved areas, although suffering little competition from other vegetation, do often suffer the effects of poor soil aeration, nutrient status and moisture relations.

The mean annual shoot extension of trees in grass was 2.0 cm less in suburban areas than in town centres (Figure 15), perhaps due to soil compaction and limited area for rooting in the grass strips between pavement and road in many residential areas. The shoot extension of trees in shrub beds was, on average, 3.9 cm greater in suburban areas than in town centres. Low numbers of such trees in suburban areas reduces the reliability of this comparison, but part of the explanation may be the comparatively low level of 'people pressures', compaction and damage, in spaces where suburban shrub plantings were often found (for example infilling

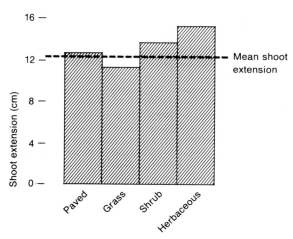

Figure 16. Mean shoot extension for all trees by planting position.

Table 2. Mean shoot extension and percentage in good condition of major species surveyed by planting position.

	Paved			Grass			Shrub		
	shoot extension (cm)		good condition (%)	shoot extension (cm)		good condition (%)	shoot extension (cm)		good condition (%)
Maple	10.4		74	9.7		82	15.2	*	86
Ash	7.3		68	11.6		76	17.7	*	93
Birch	10.7	*	79	11.3	*	82	9.8		77
Cherry	10.4	*	83	14.1	*	78	11.4	*	90
Hawthorn	14.8		62	10.8	*	91	11.2	*	100
Lime	9.6		82	11.1	*	89	12.4	*	87
Plane	15.2	*	87	17.0	*	95	13.2		75
False acacia	24.9	*	84	17.3		75	19.2	*	87
Rowan	15.4	*	82	12.7		61	13.9		73
Sycamore	7.7		79	8.4		86	12.9	*	87
Whitebeam	15.5	*	82	17.8	*	92	14.8	*	83

* survey indicates good performance in planting position specified.

planting around public buildings and in unused corners).

Despite the benefits of tree planting in shrub beds, this is not possible in many situations. Table 2 indicates, from the results of the survey, which of the commoner species groups might perform well, in terms of growth and condition, in grass or paved areas. Of the less commonly recorded species groups, beech, Italian alder, larch, oak, pear, plum, willow-leaved pear and willow may warrant wider use; not necessarily for high growth rates *per se* (although some have), but because growth rates appear not to be depressed to a great extent by planting in the more stressful environments of grass sward and paving.

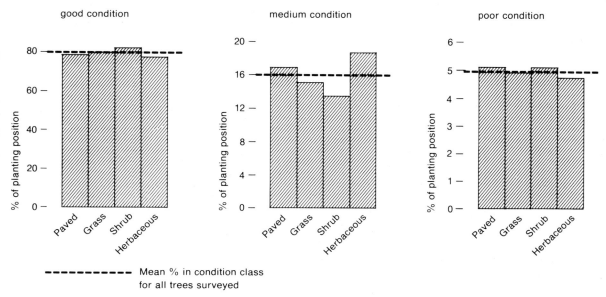

---------- Mean % in condition class
for all trees surveyed

Figure 17. Condition of all trees surveyed by planting position.

Variation in tree condition with planting position

The survey revealed little variation in the proportion of trees in good condition between planting positions (Figure 17). However, in herbaceous beds there were fewer than average trees in poor condition, but the number of trees in the medium condition category was greater than the average over all planting positions. This cannot be explained entirely by the generally younger age of the planting in this position as, if this were the case, trees in shrub beds would show a similar trend. The explanation may be damage to tree roots caused by the regular cultivation associated with herbaceous beds.

Variation in damage to trees with planting position

The incidence of the various types of tree damage was, in many cases, related to planting position (Figure 18). Damage to tree stems by vehicles, mowers and strimmers is much more frequent in paved and grass areas than in shrub or herbaceous beds. Branch dieback is more common in shrub and herbaceous beds, due mainly to the fact that a high proportion of such plantings are very recent and experiencing the dieback common on recently planted trees of large stock sizes. Of trees planted in shrub beds, only 0.7% had been vandalised compared with 1.9% of trees planted in paved areas and grass.

Soil type

Distribution

The extreme variability of urban soils and the constraint of having to sample quickly and within 0.5 m of the tree stem limited the accuracy of soil type classification. Despite this, it is notable that 98.3% of planting pit soil samples tested were of an 'unextreme' soil type. Only 0.5% of soils were classified as clay and 1.2% classified as sand.

Variation in tree growth with soil type

No relationship between shoot extension and soil type was detected in trees surveyed. This could be due in part to the small number of trees falling into the extreme categories from which to draw data.

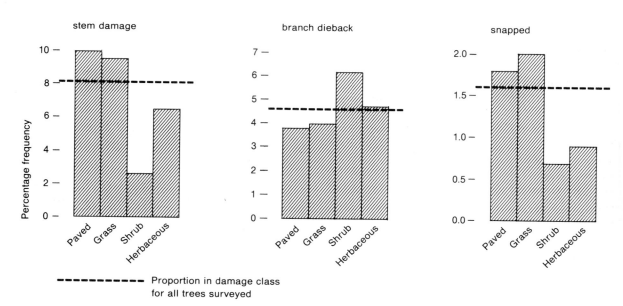

Figure 18. Damage by planting position.

Table 3. Comparison of the occurrence of genera in the 1982 and 1989 urban tree surveys.

1982		1989
1	Acer	1
2	Sorbus	2
3	Prunus	3
4	Fraxinus	7
5	Quercus	17
6	Betula	4
7	Tilia	5
8	Fagus	14
9	Salix	13
10	Alnus	11
11	Crataegus	6

Table 4. Comparison of the frequency of occurrence of genera in the 1985 and 1989 urban tree surveys.

1985		1989
1	Platanus	8
2	Acer	1
3	Sorbus	2
4	Fraxinus	7
5	Koelreuteria	not recorded
6	Populus	23
7	Alnus	11
8	Crataegus	6
9	Salix	13
10	Betula	4
11	Tilia	5

Variation in tree condition with soil type

Of trees in clay and clay loam, 88% were judged to be in good condition, along with 81% of trees in loam and sandy loam and 63% of trees in sandy soils. This trend could be related to the available water holding capacity and cation exchange capacity of the soil. Tree condition appears to have been more sensitive to these factors than shoot extension in this survey.

Discussion

In recent years two other surveys of urban trees have taken place in England, one in 1982 by the Arboricultural Advisory and Information Service (unpublished), the other in 1985 by Liverpool University (Gilbertson and Bradshaw, 1985). The 1982 survey took the form of a plant supply questionnaire to Local Authorities throughout England, and with 124 questionnaires returned this gave useful information on species being received and planted by local authorities at the time (Table 3). There is a good correlation in species incidence between the 1982 questionnaire and this survey.

The 1985 survey undertaken by Gilbertson and Bradshaw in the north of England covered 1000 recently planted trees in 11 towns. This survey found a very different distribution of species (Table 4) with, most notably, plane accounting for over 50% of the survey population.

In addition, cherry is not recorded as a significant component of the 1985 survey, despite the 1989 survey recording it as the second most common species group and occurring as frequently in the north of the country (Chesterfield and northward) as elsewhere. False acacia was also well represented in this survey but not present in any numbers in the 1985 survey. However, a low population of false acacia was recorded in the northern towns included in this survey.

The dependence on a very few genera in the urban tree population appears not to be restricted to the UK. A survey of the street trees of Brussels (Impens and Delcarte, 1979) found a dependence on the same few genera recorded in England as, to a certain extent, did Dery and Rocray (1983) in Quebec City (Table 5).

Table 5. Comparison of the frequency of occurrence of genera in Brussels (1977), Quebec (1983) and the 1989 England survey.

Brussels		England	Quebec		England	
1	Prunus	3	1	Acer	1	
2	Platanus	8	2	Betula	4	
3	Acer	1	3	Ulmus	26	
4	Robinia	9	4	Sorbus	2	
5	Tilia	5	5	Malus	10	
6	Aesculus	18	6	Quercus	17	
7	Populus	30				
8	Crataegus	6				

Table 6. Mean shoot extensions of the major species encountered on the Urban Tree Survey compared to arboreta and advanced nursery stock nursery trees.

Species	1. mean shoot extensions for nurseries and arboreta (cm)	2. mean shoot extensions for Urban Tree Survey (cm)	2 as a % of 1
Maple	22.2	11.4	51%
Cherry	16.8	11.8	70%
Rowan	24.7	13.8	56%
Birch	16.3	11.0	67%
Whitebeam	23.5	16.4	70%
Lime	15.7	10.9	69%
Ash	25.8	11.4	44%
Plane	24.9	15.5	62%
False acacia	19.6	18.9	96%
Weighted mean			58%

In order to determine the adequacy of urban tree growth rates, these rates were compared with that of trees in arboreta and advanced nursery stock nurseries (Table 6). The average shoot extension of the mean of that for nurseries and the mean of that for arboreta was used as a realistic base line. The performance of any species in the urban environment in relation to its performance in nurseries and arboreta can be used to indicate the extent to which realistic potential for growth is being achieved in the urban environment. The nine species groups considered in this way appear to be growing, on average, to 58% of their potential in the urban situation. However, only 50 nursery and aboretum trees per species group, spread between five locations, were assessed and a much larger sample would be required to draw firm conclusions.

The results of this survey relating to tree condition and mortality do not accurately depict the amount of loss and replacement that often takes place in order to achieve the establishment of successful urban trees. Two methods have been used to conduct urban tree surveys; the monitoring of particular planting sites and recently planted trees over time, and the survey undertaken at one point in time. The generally good condition of trees recorded is a finding similar to other surveys of urban trees of any age at one point in time (Table 7). Regular removal of poor

and failed trees reduces the number of such trees picked up in this type of survey. Surveys over time, however, indicate the often poor condition of recently planted stock (Plate 8) and the extent of removal and replacement required to achieve a tree population in acceptably good condition.

Although not included in the main body of this survey, 2.1% of street trees encountered were dead. Surveys monitoring particular planting sites and recently planted trees (Table 7) show better the mortality rates of recently planted urban trees (Plate 9). In the three British surveys this figure ranges from Gilbertson and Bradshaw (1985) 9.7% "of newly panted trees" (a probable underestimate), through Gilbertson and Bradshaw (1990) 23% by 3 years after planting, to Skinner (1986) 44% by 5 years after planting in a survey restricted to standard and larger sized stock.

Of the trees recorded in this survey, 1.5% had been snapped. Several of these trees could have been wind snapped but most had clearly been vandalised. Similarly, Gilbertson and Bradshaw (1985) found that 1.7% of the recently planted trees surveyed in northern England had died because of vandalism. Although rapid removal and replacement of vandalised trees would tend to reduce the number of vandalised trees picked up in either survey, vandalism appears generally to be a minor problem in urban tree estab-

14

Table 7. Summary of published urban tree surveys.

Survey and location	% in good condition	% dead	years after planting
Surveys of all urban trees			
Hodge (1991); England	80	2.1	all ages
Impens and Delcarte (1979); Brussels	97	1.9	all ages
Talarchek (1987); New Orleans	90	—	all ages
Surveys of recently planted urban trees			
Gilbertson and Bradshaw (1985); N. England	64	10†	newly planted
Gilbertson and Bradshaw (1990); Liverpool	—	23	3 years
Impens and Delcarte (1979); Brussels	85-97*	3-14*	1 year
Skinner (1986); Scotland	32	44	2 years
Nowak et al. (1990); Oakland, USA	—	34	2 years

† probable underestimate due to rapid replacement of dead trees by some local authorities.
* annual surveys carried out over 4 years.

lishment (although sometimes locally intense), despite the fact that most of the trees included in either of the surveys were of a size that could easily be damaged by vandals.

A programme of regular long-term monitoring of a number of planting positions where attempts are being made to establish trees would yield much valuable information on the number of trees planted before successful establishment is achieved, and on the extent and causes of poor condition, slow growth, damage and death. This information could be used to generate cost models of the various types of urban tree establishment using typical success rates compared to that which should be realistically achievable.

Significant branch dieback was recorded in 4.5% of trees surveyed, whilst Gilbertson and Bradshaw (1985) in their survey of 1000 recently planted trees in the north of England found 9.8% of trees surveyed showed signs of dieback, confirming the evidence of this survey that dieback in the urban situation is most commonly found on recently planted trees.

It is clear from this survey that trees planted in shrub beds generally grow better and sustain less damage and vandalism than trees in other planting positions. This has two important implications. First, much expenditure may be saved by not having to make repeated replacement of snapped trees and second, if trees are well protected by shrubs, smaller and cheaper

stock sizes might successfully be used to establish urban trees even in street situations. Other advantages of tree planting in shrub beds include reduced interference with underground services (by concentrating tree planting into beds) and the possible reduction of herbicide useage (as shrubs suppress aggressive weed growth and as the weed-free area required around trees in grass for ease of grass maintenance is not required in shrub beds). Urban and suburban redevelopment in many inner-cities and the increasing use of bottlenecks and sharp corners to reduce traffic speed should create more opportunities for informal planting of urban trees in shrub beds (Plate 10).

Conclusions and recommendations

With a mean shoot extension of trees surveyed of 12.4 cm (about 60% of what could reasonably be expected, compared with trees in nurseries and arboreta) and with 80% of trees in good condition, this urban tree survey indicates that the majority of established urban trees are visually improving the urban landscape, although this role would be more rapidly fulfilled if growth rates were improved. Other surveys indicate that the situation for recently planted trees is much worse.

15

Reliance on a very few species groups in urban situations is not justified in many areas, particularly as the limitations thought to be imposed by air quality are being removed with increasing control of industrial and vehicular emissions and development of pedestrian precincts and bypasses. The use of a greater range of species where appropriate, including those showing good growth rates from this survey, should be encouraged both to further enhance the urban environment and to reduce the impact of possible tree pest and disease epidemics.

The survey has highlighted the generally young age of the urban tree population; emphasising the importance of the maintenance of existing mature trees and the protection, from development and other urban pressures, of maturing specimens. The survey has also shown the poor condition of, and frequency of branch dieback on, surviving recently planted urban trees. This is partly due to the hostile planting environment, but the condition of young trees could be improved by better site preparation, careful species choice, the use of smaller stock sizes where possible, and appropriate and regular maintenance.

Of trees surveyed, 15% showed significant damage, principally damage to the base of the stem and branch dieback. Much stem damage was assessed to be due to poor maintenance practices (such as not removing stakes and ties, and tree damage by mowers, strimmers and herbicides). Evidence of vandalism was relatively uncommon and appears to be less of a problem than is popularly believed. The use of large stock sizes and substantial tree guards rarely deter, and often challenge, the determined vandal. The low level of vandalism recorded would suggest that cheaper types of planting stock and less elaborate protective measures could be successfuly used in some situations.

The survey has found a predominant, but reducing, trend of trees planted in grass sward and an increasing trend toward tree planting in shrub beds. Tree planting in shrub beds confers benefits of increased growth rates and reduced damage, and may further enable smaller, cheaper stock sizes to be successfully established.

It is possibly surprising that trees recorded were, on average, growing better in paved areas than in grass, as paved areas are generally considered to be the most testing urban environment. Birch, cherry, hawthorn, plane, false acacia, rowan and whitebeam appear, from the survey, to be the more successful of the commonly recorded species for paved or grass areas.

REFERENCES

DERY, ROCRAY ET ASSOCIES (1983). Problems affecting urban trees in Quebec City. *Journal of Arboriculture* **9** (6), 167–169.

GILBERTSON, P. and BRADSHAW, A.D. (1985). Tree survival in cities: the extent and nature of the problem. *Arboricultural Journal* **9** (2), 131–142.

GILBERTSON, P. and BRADSHAW, A.D. (1990). The survival of newly planted trees in inner cities. *Arboricultural Journal* **14** (4), 287–310.

IMPENS, R.A. and DELCARTE, E. (1979). Survey of urban trees in Brussels, Belgium. *Journal of Arboriculture* **5** (8), 169–175.

HODGE, S.J. and WHITE, J.E.J. (1990). *The ultimate size and spread of trees commonly grown in towns.* Arboriculture Research Note 84/90/ARB. DoE Arboricultural Advisory and Information Service, Forestry Commission, Edinburgh.

NOWAK, D.J., McBRIDE, J.R. and BEATTY, R.A. (1990). Newly planted street tree growth and mortality. *Journal of Arboriculture* **16** (5), 124–129.

SKINNER, D.N. (1986). *Planting success rates – standard trees.* Arboriculture Research Note 66/86/SILS. DoE Arboricultural Advisory and Information Service, Forestry Commission, Edinburgh.

TALARCHEK, G. M. (1987). Indicators of urban forest condition in New Orleans. *Journal of Arboriculture* **13** (9), 217–225.

Appendix 1

Full list of species groups surveyed, their frequency of occurrence and mean shoot extension

Species group	Number of trees recorded	Mean shoot extension (cm) and (standard error)	Details
Maple	563	11.4 (±0.36)	All *Acers* except *A. pseudoplatanus*
Cherry	461	11.8 (±0.42)	All *Prunus* except *P. avium, P. cerasifera, P. dulcis* and *P. padus*
Rowan	373	13.8 (±0.59)	All *Sorbus* with pinnate leaves
Birch	292	11.0 (±0.36)	All *Betula*
Whitebeam	288	16.4 (±0.55)	All whitebeams
Lime	214	10.9 (±0.41)	All *Tilia*
Sycamore	213	8.6 (±0.50)	*Acer pseudoplatanus*
Ash	110	11.4 (±0.76)	All *Fraxinus*
Plane	102	15.5 (±0.99)	All *Platanus*
Hawthorn	94	12.6 (±0.92)	All hawthorns
False acacia	94	18.9 (±1.29)	*Robinia* and *Gleditsia*
Common alder	69	10.8 (±0.58)	*Alnus glutinosa*
Hornbeam	66	8.2 (±0.55)	All *Carpinus*
Beech	53	10.1 (±0.97)	All *Fagus*
Cypress	51	11.8 (±0.57)	All *Chamaecyparis* and *Cupressus*
Crab apple	48	9.8 (±1.07)	All *Malus* except *M.* 'John Downie'
Wild cherry	48	18.4 (±1.24)	*Prunus avium*
Willow	44	25.8 (±1.68)	*Salix* excluding *S. alba* 'Tristis'
Pine	42	6.8 (±0.58)	All *Pinus*
Apple	42	10.2 (±1.16)	*Malus* 'John Downie'
Plum	40	13.0 (±1.08)	*Prunus cerasifera*
Oak	40	6.7 (±0.69)	All *Quercus*
Horse chestnut	39	12.2 (±1.27)	All *Aesculus*
Cockspur thorn	26	6.8 (±0.75)	*Crataegus prunifolia*
Laburnum	20	6.8 (±1.74)	All *Laburnum*
Elm	19	9.7 (±1.67)	All *Ulmus*
Holly	17	5.7 (±0.61)	All *Ilex*
Pear	15	8.9 (±1.98)	All *Pyrus* except *P. salicifolia*
Weeping willow	14	56.6 (±5.79)	*Salix alba* 'Tristis'
Poplar	14	11.0 (±1.62)	All *Populus*
Spruce	12	5.6 (±0.70)	All *Picea*
Italian alder	11	24.2 (±2.20)	*Alnus cordata*
Bird cherry	8	16.0 (±3.05)	*Prunus padus*
Hazel	8	7.7 (±2.03)	All *Corylus*
Larch	7	15.7 (±1.97)	All *Larix*
Fir	6	4.5 (±0.42)	All *Abies*
Snowy mespilus	6	8.0 (±2.19)	*Amelanchier laevis*
Caucasian elm	5	25.8 (±8.76)	All *Zelkova*

Species group	Number of trees recorded	Mean shoot extension (cm) and (standard error)	Details
Tulip tree	4	6.6 (±1.34)	All *Liriodendron*
Dove tree	4	13.6 (±1.10)	*Davidia involucrata*
Almond	3	3.5 (±1.01)	*Prunus dulcis*
Indian bean tree	3	14.4 (±1.87)	All *Catalpa*
Elder	2	9.0 (±0.25)	All *Sambucus*
Douglas fir	2	5.1 (±0.70)	*Pseudotsuga menziesii*
Medlar	2	27.7 (±3.10)	*Mespilus germanica*
Sweet chestnut	2	7.8 (±0.90)	*Castanea sativa*
Juniper	1	4.6	All *Juniperus*
Sumac	1	32.0	All *Rhus*
Willow-leaved pear	1	29.0	*Pyrus salicifolia*
Yew	1	6.8	All *Taxus*

Printed in the United Kingdom for HMSO
Dd.0293215 6/91 C25